123
SESAME STREET

HIDE&SEEK
NEAR&FAR

Illustrated by Sue DiCicco

pi kids

publications international, ltd.

Round and round our planet twirls,
As Grover travels around the world!
Now he wants to play a game
That everywhere is played the same —
Hide-and-seek! But he needs a hand.
Who's hiding in the DESERT sand?

Find these
while you look
for Elmo!

Camel (this one!)

Canteen

Snake

Archaeologist

Goat (this one!)

Now Elmo's at our second stop.
It's up among the MOUNTAIN tops.
Help him out, but take your time.
Find his pal who's on a climb.

Find these while you look for Grover!

Mountain climber

Monk

Yak
(this one!)

Lhasa Apso

Snow
leopard

In TOWN, Grover spots a busy street
And is excited by the friends he meets.
It's Chinese New Year! Can you spy
The red-footed friend parading by?

Find these
while you look
for Elmo!

Civet

Panda

Bamboo

Rickshaw

Dragon

Now Elmo's in the OUTBACK, mate!
The sun is hot, the view is great.
Walk about to the river's end
To find a hopping, hidden friend.

Find these
while you look
for Grover!

Boomerang

Kookaburra

Emu
(this one!)

Didgeridoo

Crocodile

Trees and leaves and steamy brush,
Grover's in a FOREST lush.
With birds and green stuff everywhere,
It's tough to spot Elmo over there!

Find these
while you
look for Elmo!

Jaguar

Orchid

Mango

Sloth

Snake
(this one!)

Butterfly (this one!)

Tall trees hide a grassy MEADOW,
Where Grover also hides from Elmo!
While you search for a small snowflake,
Can you find Grover by the lake?

Find these while you look for Grover!

Leaf
(this one!)

Mountie

Snowflake
(this one!)

Pinecone

Loon

Grover visits this big CITY,
Its bustling streets are oh-so-pretty.
He spies busy people all around,
But not where Elmo can be found!

Find these
while you look
for Elmo!

Mime

Painter

Fountain

Bread
(this one!)

Student

Note to Parents:

Here are interactive learning ideas to use with this book. Each activity focuses on a different bit of knowledge, from colors to counting to learning about different types of wildlife. You and your child will probably come up with even more ideas for Look and Find activities as you read together.

TIBET

Climb back onto the snowy MOUNTAIN and help your child count how many of each colored flag there are:

red

yellow

blue

green

white

EGYPT

Head back to the DESERT with your child, and ask him or her to count how many of each item there are:

mummies   scorpions

camels   goats

pyramids   people

dates (a fruit)

CHINA

Explain to your child that in China, 12 animals are often used to show years on the calendar. Then ask your child to find each one somewhere in TOWN:

rat   dragon   monkey

ox   snake   rooster

tiger   horse   dog

rabbit   sheep   pig

AUSTRALIA

The OUTBACK has many animals that can't be found anywhere else in the world, except in zoos. Help point out these different animals:

echidna   wombat   bandicoot

platypus   koala   kangaroo

COSTA RICA

The rain FOREST has lots and lots and lots of birds. Help your child find each of these feathered friends:

woodpecker   heron   hummingbird

Resplendent Quetzal   toucan   Scarlet Macaw

CANADA

Mammals are animals that have hair or fur. Humans are mammals, and so are puppies. Look in the MEADOW for these furry animals:

bear   moose   timber wolf
deer   otter   fox
bobcat

FRANCE

Every CITY in every country has its own special places to see. Help your child look for these buildings found in Paris:

Arc de Triomphe   Bastille   Eiffel Tower

Notre Dame Cathedral   Louvre   Basilica du Sacre Coeur

Elmo loves to learn about colors — and there's
no place where learning is more colorful than
Sesame Street! Help the furry red monster
and his neighbors look for the colorful
things that can be found everywhere!

ELMO&FRIENDS

Illustrated by DiCicco Studios

Roses are red, and Elmo is, too. There are so many red things and so much to do. What else is red? Look around and you'll see. Get ready to giggle…some are silly!

Big Bird loves yellow. He likes how it looks. Look for yellow in some pictures he took.

Zoe wears a pink tutu in this ballet. What other pink things can you see? Can you say?

HELLO, EVERYBODY!
Like grass, Grover's new
sunglasses are green.
Can you find these other
green things he's seen?

"One wonderful purple number one!" says the Count. What other purple things are parading about?

Cookie Monster's dream is sugary-sweet! Look for these blue things on this cookie-filled street.

Ernie's fixing food of all different types. Look for these things he has used that have stripes.

Note to parents: Here are interactive learning ideas to use with this book. Each activity focuses on a different skill, from naming animals to counting to learning the alphabet. You and your child will probably come up with even more ideas for Look and Find activities as you read together.

ELMO: ANIMALS

Ask your child to point out all of these animals and animal shapes.

mouse
bird slippers
rubber duckie
butterfly
bird
dog
kitten
bug

BIG BIRD: PARTS OF THE BODY

Point to pictures and ask your child to name parts of the body.

hair (Bert)   nose (Elmo)
ear (Count)   mouth (Betty Lou)
hand (Ernie)   eyes (Grover)
tail (Snuffy)   feet (Big Bird)

THE COUNT: COUNTING

There are lots of things to count. Admire how many of these things your child can spot and count.

bananas (8)
striped party hats (16)
roller skates (5)
tennis rackets (3)
pogo sticks (2)
red balloons (4)
clowns (3)
birds (11)
twiddlebugs (7)

ZOE: MATCHING

No two real snowflakes are alike. But there are matching pairs in Zoe's show! Help your child find all 13 pairs by pointing out shapes they share.

GROVER: GOING TO THE BEACH

Your child can help Grover find these fun things to take to the beach.

beach ball
sand pail
sand shovel

straw hat
snorkel & mask
sun lotion

ERNIE AND BERT: THE ALPHABET

Look around the picture together, to find things that start with or look like each letter in the alphabet.

(For example, for A, there is an apple and an apron. There's a Q made of whipped cream. For V, find a vase. Crossed spoons form an X.) Cheer when your child thinks up a funny or surprising letter-picture connection.

COOKIE MONSTER: STARTS WITH C

Cookie begins with C. Ask your child what other things in the picture start with C.

cat
cactus
candy cane
crown
corn
cake
cane
cap
cape

car
canoe
carrot
clock
cup
coins
cow
candles
can (garbage)

Elmo is growing up, and so are you!
One big part of getting bigger and older
is using the potty. Follow Elmo into the
bathroom and find out all about it as
you look for all the fun and colorful
things hidden in each scene.

ELMO'S POTTY TIME

Illustrated by Tom Brannon

You know what's so great about learning to use the potty? Getting to wear underwear, just like a big kid! Underwear is everywhere! Look for these colorful pairs.

Elmo went into his bathroom. There was a big potty and a little potty, too. It's a special potty that Elmo decorated himself! Find these other bathroom things.

Sometimes Elmo is so busy playing that he doesn't remember to use the potty. But Elmo's mommy reminds him to listen to his body. Find these things that Elmo can play with when he finishes using the bathroom.

"Bathroom time!" says Mrs. Graham, Elmo's preschool teacher. She is there if anyone needs help in the bathroom. Point to these school things all around Elmo's classroom.

Elmo even uses the potty when he visits his friends, like the Count. And he always remembers to wipe, flush, and wash. *"Ah-ah-ah!"* says the Count. "Count to twenty as you wash your hands! Then find these batty things in my bathroom."

Oops! Elmo was so busy playing with Zoe that he forgot to go potty. But it was okay. Accidents happen. Elmo's mommy helped him get cleaned up. Find these things that Elmo can play with.

Congratulations!
You're using the potty and
wearing big-kid underwear!
Elmo knew you could do it!

CERTIFICATE
SEAL OF APPROVAL
OK

CONGRATULATIONS!
YOU DID IT!

POTTY

MATCHING

Turn to Elmo's unbelievable underwear page and ask your child to point to six matching pairs of underwear.

PHONICS

B-A-T-H-R-O-O-M. That's how Elmo spells bathroom! Ask your child to find things in Elmo's bathroom that start with each letter of the word.

B - Boat, Brush, Book, Basket
A - Apple
T - Toilet, Towel, Tub
H - House, Hairspray
R - Robot, Radio, Rug, Rubber Duckie
O - Owl
O - Orange
M - Mirror, Mommy, Monster

SHAPES

Ask your child to search the playground for these shapes.

Circle
Triangle
Diamond/Rhombus
Square
Octagon
Rectangle
Oval

PATTERNS

Return to Elmo's preschool and ask your child to point out these patterns in the classroom.

Rug
Xylophone
Leaves
ABCs
Painting
Stack of books
Checkerboard floor

COUNTING

Flap your wings and fly back to the Count's bathroom. Ask your child to count how many of each of these things there are.

Cats (1)
Spiders (2)
Lightning bolts (3)
Towels (4)
Brown bats (5)

SPATIAL RELATIONS

Ask your child to look around Elmo's house for things that are:

Over
Under
Inside
Next to
Behind
In front of

ANIMALS

Turn to Elmo's Potty Party and ask your child to point to these animals (and make their animal sounds, too).

Bear
Dog
Elephant
Horse
Monkey
Seal
Tiger

There are many things that Elmo has
learned to do as he gets bigger.
These are things that you can do, too!
Go along with Elmo and his Sesame
Street friends as they grow up and
have new adventures, looking for
all the fun stuff along the way!

I CAN DO IT!

Illustrated by Bob Berry

COLORS

Hip hip hooray! First day of school!
So much to see and do.
Zoe's excited to play and learn.
She can do it, and so can you!

Look for these things in Zoe's classroom.

A splashy way to beat the heat —
Swimming lessons at the pool!
Just like Elmo, Grover, and Zoe,
You can do it! It'll be cool!

Look for these swimming things.

Cleaning teeth, brightening smiles —
That's what dentists do.
Say "Ahh!" and show those pearly whites!
The Count can do it — you can, too!

Look for these dental things.

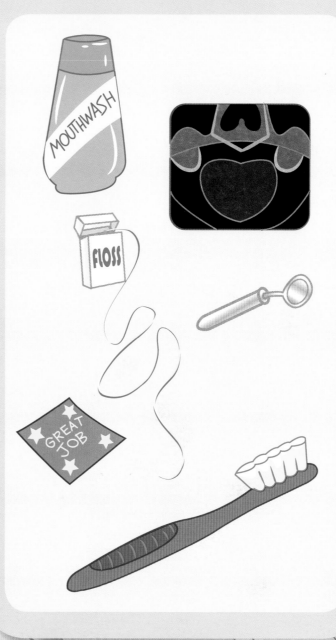

So many ways to go on wheels,
On four or three or two.
Elmo zooms around the park.
He can do it, so can you!

Look for these things that go.

"Happy birthday, Cookie Monster!"
That's what Elmo and Zoe say.
Celebrate a party for a friend.
You can do it — happy birthday!

Look for these party things.

HAPPY BIRTHDAY
COOKIE

All tucked in, the room is dark,
But the moon is shining bright.
Elmo falls asleep in bed.
You can do it, too. Good night!

Look for these nighttime things.

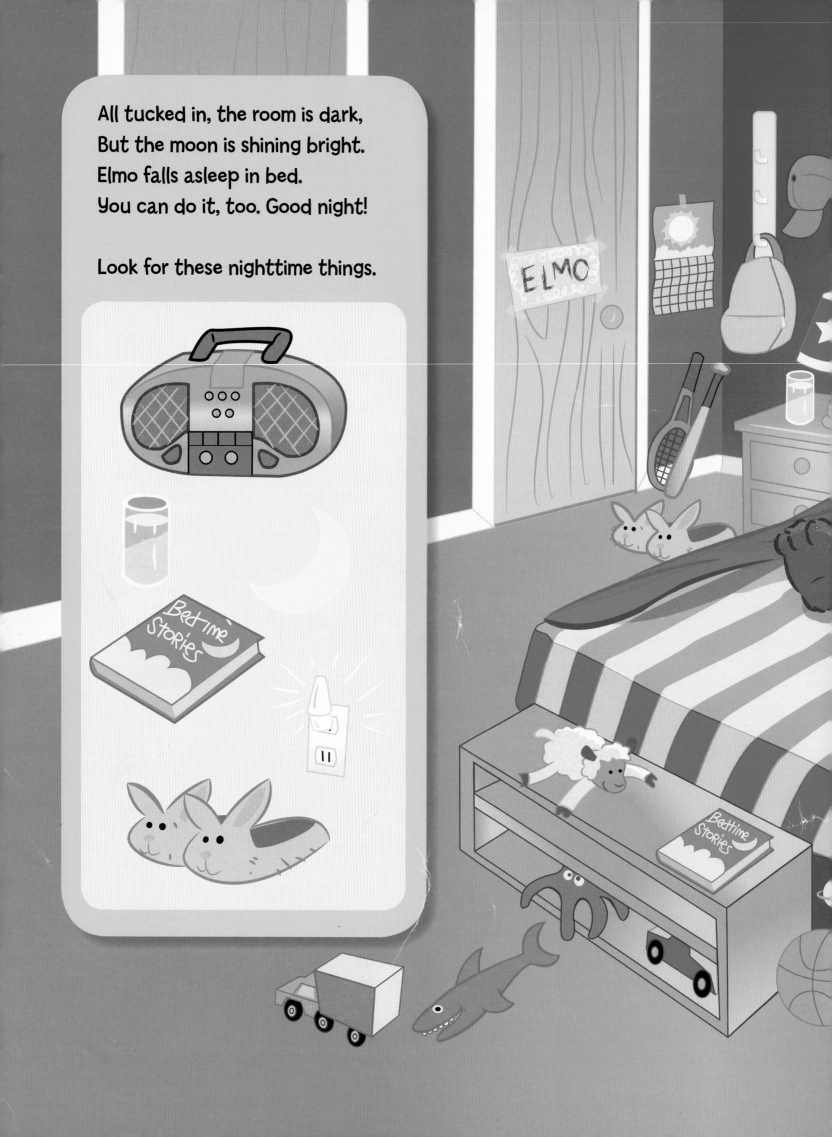

Note to Parents:

Here are additional interactive learning activities for you and your child. Each activity focuses on a different skill, from counting to rhyming to recognizing patterns that occur in nature. You and your child will probably come up with even more ideas for Look and Find activities as you read together.

MATCHING

Ask your child to match these pairs of objects in the classroom:

- Toy balls
- Teddy bears
- Boxes of crayons
- Twin boys
- Toy dinosaurs
- Toy cars

RELATIONAL CONCEPTS

Ask your child to look around the swimming pool to find:

- Which beach ball is **bigger** and which one is **smaller?**
- Which chair is **taller** and which one is **shorter?**
- Which end of the pool is **deep** and which one is **shallow?**
- Which umbrella is **open** and which one is **closed?**

COUNTING

Ask your child to count the following dental items:

- 3 tubes of toothpaste
- 2 dental helpers
- 4 toothbrushes
- 2 monsters